HOW IN THE WORLD? STUDY GUIDE

by PAUL BENJAMIN

WALNUT GROVE CHRISTIAN CHURCH
RURAL ROUTE 1
ARCOLA, IL 61910

American Church Growth
Study Series

 STANDARD PUBLISHING
Cincinnati, Ohio   4036

AMERICAN
CHURCH GROWTH
STUDY SERIES

by Paul Benjamin

COMPLETED STUDIES:

THE GROWING CONGREGATION
with
STUDY GUIDE

HOW IN THE WORLD?
with
STUDY GUIDE and MINIBOOK SERIES

THE EQUIPPING MINISTRY
with
STUDY GUIDE

The **American Church Growth Study Series** was initiated in 1972 with the publication of *THE GROWING CONGREGATION* and its companion *STUDY GUIDE* by Lincoln Christian College Press.

A concept-changing book, *THE GROWING CONGREGATION* has now been used by hundreds of churches. It is written about the basic idea that a non-growing congregation needs to take a sharp look at itself in light of patterns of growth in the New Testament. Consequently, it accents basic Biblical principles of growth which must be applied today for effective growing churches.

Basically a "content-oriented study," *THE GROWING CONGREGATION* was joined in 1973 by an "action-oriented book" entitled *HOW IN THE WORLD?* Donald A. McGavran wrote the foreword.

This second study concentrates on the "how" in evangelism. It includes chapters on analyzing the community, making a witness-survey, and guidelines for presenting the gospel to others. The appendix of this book contains details about the way a congregation can conduct its own "Care-Promise Service."

In 1975, Standard Publishing began producing the entire series. Also during this year, *HOW IN THE WORLD?* appeared in seven mini-books. Each book deals with a specific area of evangelism and provides a shirt-pocket-size guide for on-the-job training. Standard printed the Witness-Survey cards and the Care-Promise cards to accompany the series. A companion *STUDY GUIDE* is also available.

In 1976, World-Wide Publications made available a cassette series to accompany the American Church Growth Study Series. The series includes two major addresses and two seminars on Chruch Growth. These cassettes were sent out to all who registered for the National Consultation on Church Growth.

THE EQUIPPING MINISTRY and its *STUDY-GUIDE* is the third book in the series. This book is written in an effort to help churches practice the ministry of all believers. It is written with the view that world evangelization is only an empty dream unless the preaching ministry can return to its primary task—equipping the saints for ministry. At the back of this book are a series of "steps" for implementing these studies in the congregation.

USING THE AMERICAN CHURCH GROWTH
STUDY SERIES

The texts in the American Church Growth Study Series are now proven tools in helping churches grow. Many congregations have been revitalized by following the principles of church growth which the author sets forth in this series.

Your effectiveness, in following one of the major texts, will be greatly multiplied if you use the *Study Guide* in a classroom setting. Continually offering these studies to new groups in the church will help produce an accumulative effect.

How to Study This Course

As you approach the textbook, (1) read it rapidly all the way through to gain an overview of its major ideas. (2) Read each portion carefully, reflecting on the implications in every paragraph and sentence. The material was written with care and should be read the same way. (3) In the *STUDY GUIDE,* answer the questions by restating the ideas from the text in your own words. (4) Check your statements for accuracy by referring back to the text. (5) Think through again any ideas which are not clear to you.

Who Can Use This Course

The textbook and *STUDY GUIDE* may be used either by individuals or as a resource for various study groups. Studying with other people will, however, enhance the effectiveness of learning. Sunday-school classes may use this course as an elective for a quarter. Other existing study groups will find benefits in devoting a series of sessions to it. If you do not already have an opportunity for studying with a class or group, why not invite several others to meet with you for study and discussion. If you are a group leader, make certain that each member of the group has a copy of the text and the *STUDY GUIDE.*

How to Use the Study Guide With a Group

If you are studying with others in a class or group, work through an agreed-upon portion of the textbook before each session. Write out the answers to the related questions in the *STUDY GUIDE.* Do not simply copy passages from the text as answers. State the ideas in your own words. In class, discuss ideas from the text and compare the ways you have stated your answers. Re-examine the text where views differ. Seek to arrive at complete clarity of ideas and to make specific application to your own lives and to your congregation.

How to Use the Study Guide for Individual Study

If you are studying on your own, the *STUDY GUIDE* will serve a particularly important function. After carefully reading a portion of the text, lay it aside and write your answers to the related questions in the *STUDY GUIDE.* Then check your answers by comparing them with the pertinent passages of the textbook. A key for locating sections of the text that deal specifically with each question is found on pages 28 and 29. Study with a view to applying the ideas through action.

Measuring Results

The results of this study can best be measured in terms of their influence upon the actual practices of your congregation. What changes are you initiating? How many additional people are involved in ministry? How has this study affected the lifestyle of your church? These are some questions to help you determine the initial results of this study.

The long range results should be measured after sufficient time has elapsed for these ideas to become activated in the church and community.

Joe Ellis, Ph.D.
Pacific Christian College
Fullerton, California

1

THE UNFULFILLED COMMISSION

1. After commissioning the disciples to be his witnesses, why did Jesus instruct them to return to Jerusalem?

_____

_____

_____

_____

2. Did Jesus practice an *inclusive* or *exclusive* ministry? Explain.

_____

_____

_____

_____

3. List some of the obstacles the early Christians faced when they told others about their faith.

_____

_____

_____

_____

4. Why did the fire of faith spread so rapidly?

_____

_____

_____

_____

_____

5. Discuss the second "teach" of the Great Commission.

_____

_____

_____

_____

_____

6. What impressed the pagans about the early Christians?

_____

_____

_____

_____

7. Why does evangelism require determination by the congregation?

_____

_____

_____

_____

_____

8. How does a concern for quantity enhance congregational life?

_____

_____

_____

_____

_____

9. Comment on the statement, "Evangelism in the New Testament was never in the hands of a few paid professionals."

_____

_____

_____

_____

10. Why are so many people plodding wearily through an earthly existence?

_____

_____

_____

_____

11. Is it possible for the Great Commission to be fulfilled in our generation? Explain.

_____

_____

_____

_____

12. What does Habakkuk 2:14 promise?

_____

_____

_____

_____

_____

ANALYZING THE COMMUNITY

1. Comment on the statement, "Evangelism never takes place in a vacuum."

_____

_____

_____

_____

2. What can congregations learn from the business world?

_____

_____

_____

_____

3. List some natural geographical boundaries when a church selects an area of concern.

_____

_____

_____

_____

4. Explain the suggestion of a three-mile radius for geographical outreach.

_____

_____

_____

_____

5. How should a congregation react to a subculture in their area of concern?

_____

_____

_____

_____

6. Describe the simplest way of making a sociological survey of an area.

_____

_____

_____

_____

_____

7. Why should congregations in changing neighborhoods start daughter churches in their area?

_____

_____

_____

_____

8. What is a population pyramid? Describe briefly its usefulness.

_____

_____

_____

_____

_____

9. How can a demographic analysis of a community save a congregation from misdirected evangelistic effort?

_____

_____

_____

_____

10. What are the usual prominent age groups in (1) rural areas, (2) urban areas, and (3) the suburbs?

_____

_____

_____

_____

11. Explain how the predominate denomination helps influence the basic attitudes of a community.

_____

_____

_____

_____

12. Action-assignment: Make a partial analysis of your community by following one of the four categories suggested in this chapter.

3

MAKING A WITNESS SURVEY

1. What does Acts 20:20 suggest?

_____

_____

_____

_____

_____

2. Why is it wise in some circumstances to notify city officials before a survey?

_____

_____

_____

_____

3. Why are some church members reluctant to participate in any kind of religious survey?

_____

_____

_____

_____

4. Discuss the statement, "The demands of love cannot be fulfilled without knowledge."

_____

_____

_____

_____

5. Give a reason for each surveyor including a personal testimony about Christ.

_____

_____

_____

_____

6. Cite the advantages and disadvantages of working with a partner during a survey.

_____

_____

_____

_____

_____

7. What is the block plan?

_____

_____

_____

_____

8. Why is it important to keep a double file on the callees?

_____

_____

_____

_____

_____

_____

9. What can be done during a worship service to find people who need the ministry of the church?

_____

_____

_____

_____

10. Why will non-religious parents allow their children to receive Christian teaching?

_____

_____

_____

_____

11. Can any system of scheduled questing compensate for the need of spontaneous witnessing? Explain.

_____

_____

_____

_____

12. Action-assignment: Participate in a witness-survey. Report your experience.

_____

_____

_____

_____

_____

4

UNDERSTANDING THE UNCOMMITTED

1. Approximately how many persons living in North America are uncommitted to the Christian faith?

_____

_____

_____

_____

2. Why do Christians need to be familiar with the basic thought patterns of those who live outside the Christian faith?

_____

_____

_____

_____

3. How can those who were formerly "of the world" serve as valuable resource personnel to a congregation?

_____

_____

_____

_____

4. Explain the difference between "in the world" and "of the world."

_____

_____

_____

_____

5. Why are Christians foolish to envy those who live lives of unrighteousness?

_____

_____

_____

_____

6. Why is the idea of the strong person who "makes it" in life a myth?

_____

_____

_____

_____

7. What is the tremendous power of the gospel of Jesus Christ?

_____

_____

_____

_____

_____

8. Why was the resurrection of Jesus so prominent in the preaching of early Christians?

_____

_____

_____

_____

_____

9. How has death been defeated?

_____

_____

_____

_____

_____

10. What is the "double edge" of urbanization?

_____

_____

_____

_____

_____

11. Explain the statement, "Man is free not to choose God."

_____

_____

_____

_____

_____

12. Action-assignment: Talk to someone who is uncommitted to Christ and try to understand his/her reasoning. Report your findings.

_____

_____

_____

_____

5

GUIDELINES FOR WITNESSING

1. Why are many Christians reluctant to speak to others about Christ?

   _____

   _____

   _____

   _____

2. Can a model for witnessing be devised which covers all the facets of calling? Explain.

   _____

   _____

   _____

   _____

3. What are the advantages in following some kind of mental guidelines?

   _____

   _____

   _____

   _____

4. Read the account of the conversion of the Ethiopian in Acts 8:35-39. Tell in your own words what happened.

   _____

   _____

   _____

   _____

5. What is usually the first step in approaching another person with the gospel?

_____

_____

_____

_____

6. Discuss the importance of talking about "them"—the callees.

_____

_____

_____

_____

_____

7. Does unfriendliness on the part of the callees always mean a rejection of the gospel? Explain.

_____

_____

_____

_____

8. Why is it false to assume that everyone in America has already heard the gospel?

_____

_____

_____

_____

_____

9. State the three main ideas of the Golden Text.

_____

_____

_____

_____

_____

10. Why is it important for new Christians to find a happy congregational home?

_____

_____

_____

_____

11. Comment on the statement, "The person committed to Christ lives a different type of life from the worldling."

_____

_____

_____

_____

12. Action-assignment: Speak to someone about Christ and follow the *Witnessing Triangle.* Report on the results.

_____

_____

_____

_____

_____

6

CALLED TO MINISTER

1. Do all our troubles end when we accept Christ? Explain.

   _____

   _____

   _____

   _____

2. What are the benefits of a special class for new people?

   _____

   _____

   _____

   _____

   _____

3. Mention some of the basic problems with the "checkpoint" system.

   _____

   _____

   _____

   _____

   _____

4. Why is Christian freedom so important?

   _____

   _____

   _____

   _____

5. Give some of the reasons why newcomers to a community are reluctant to affiliate with a local congregation.

_____

_____

_____

_____

6. How should Christians react to new families in the community?

_____

_____

_____

_____

_____

7. Discuss the statement, "Changes are seldom made in the life of the church without tension."

_____

_____

_____

_____

8. Why should Sunday morning worship be looked upon as a meeting of the ministers of the church?

_____

_____

_____

_____

_____

9. Why is it wrong to expect Christians in the pews to minister without providing help?

_____

_____

_____

_____

10. What kind of reorientation must many pulpit ministers experience before they seriously consider training ministers in the pews?

_____

_____

_____

_____

11. What can be done about the seeds of discord which often sprout between newer and older members in the church?

_____

_____

_____

_____

12. Action-assignment: Write up a job description of either (1) A ministry you now have in the church, (2) A ministry you want to develop. Use the page provided at the back of the *Study Guide.*

7

EMPOWERED BY THE SPIRIT

1. What promise did Jesus give the disciples after He commanded them to evangelize?

_____

_____

_____

_____

2. Why does the word "prophesy" usually require an explanation?

_____

_____

_____

_____

3. Give another title for *The Acts of the Apostles.*

_____

_____

_____

_____

4. Does the Holy Spirit call attention to himself or to Christ? Explain.

_____

_____

_____

_____

_____

5. Is it necessary for fear to be completely conquered before a person evangelizes?

_____

_____

_____

_____

6. List some advantages in calling "two by two."

_____

_____

_____

_____

_____

7. Why must we continue to combat fear?

_____

_____

_____

_____

_____

8. Discuss the statement, "No worker in the harvest needs to feel for one moment he is alone."

_____

_____

_____

_____

_____

9. Why are the writers of the New Testament concerned about spiritual maturity?

_____

_____

_____

_____

10. What keeps some Christians from experiencing the power of the Holy Spirit in their lives?

_____

_____

_____

_____

11. What is the basis for much of the current optimism about world evangelization?

_____

_____

_____

_____

12. Action-assignment: Use a concordance and read all the references in the New Testament which mention the Holy Spirit.

KEY TO ANSWERS

1

THE UNFULFILLED COMMISSION

1. p. 1	5. p. 4	9. p. 7
2. p. 1	6. pp. 4&5	10. p. 8
3. pp. 2&3	7. p. 6	11. p. 8
4. p. 3	8. p. 7	12. p. 8

2

ANALYZING THE COMMUNITY

1. p. 9	5. p. 13	9. p. 15
2. p. 9	6. p. 13	10. p. 15
3. p. 11	7. p. 13	11. p. 16
4. p. 11	8. p. 13	12. p. 17

3

MAKING A WITNESS SURVEY

1. p. 18	5. p. 20	9. p. 25
2. p. 18	6. p. 23	10. p. 26
3. p. 18	7. p. 23	11. p. 26
4. p. 19	8. p. 24	12. -

4

UNDERSTANDING THE UNCOMMITTED

1. p. 28	5. p. 32	9. p. 34
2. p. 28	6. p. 33	10. p. 35
3. p. 28	7. p. 33	11. p. 36
4. p. 30	8. p. 34	12. -

5

GUIDELINES FOR WITNESSING

1. p. 37	5. p. 39	9. p. 43
2. p. 38	6. p. 41	10. p. 47
3. p. 38	7. p. 41	11. p. 47&48
4. -	8. p. 42	12. p. 38

6

CALLED TO MINISTER

1. p. 49	5. p. 52	9. p. 55
2. p. 50	6. p. 53	10. p. 56
3. p. 51	7. p. 54	11. p. 57
4. p. 51	8. p. 55	12. -

7

EMPOWERED BY THE SPIRIT

1. p. 58	5. p. 61	9. p. 64
2. p. 59	6. p. 62	10. p. 65
3. p. 60	7. p. 62	11. p. 65&66
4. p. 60	8. p. 63	12. -

STEPS TO USING THE AMERICAN CHURCH GROWTH STUDY SERIES

A Preliminary Observation

Church growth often begins in the hearts and minds of a few committed Christians. Tired of the "business as usual" routine in many American congregations, a handful of Christians believe God wants the church to grow. With this firm foundation, coupled with a spirit of fervent prayer, they look for resources to help them.

The materials in the American Church Growth Study Series are now proven instruments in assisting congregations in church growth. Some congregations have doubled in size during one year by following these ideas. Others have shown substantial gains with a dramatic increase in new members. I suggest the following steps in utilizing this series.

Step One

Set up a study class using *THE GROWING CONGREGATION* as a basic text. Your results will be multiplied if you utilize the *STUDY GUIDE* with each member. If the class meets during the traditional 13 week Sunday School quarter, plan to cover a chapter every two weeks. For example, present Chapter One the first week, ("Church Growth and the New Testament Congregations"). During the second week, fill out the *STUDY GUIDE* for that chapter. (Preferably outside the classroom). Then allow ample time for class discussion.

Remember, a congregation cannot operate from a viewpoint in church growth which it does not possess. These ideas must flow through the life of the church if you expect results.

Step Two

Plan a Care-Promise Service. See the Appendix of *THE GROWING CONGREGATION* and *HOW IN THE WORLD?* for instructions.

Step Three

Involve those who respond to the Care-Promise Service in a study of *HOW IN THE WORLD?* along with its companion *STUDY GUIDE.* Begin your program of calling in the community. We have discovered through our studies that the best time to call for Christ in America is on Saturday morning from 10:00 to 12:00. The following schedule may be followed or adapted:

9:00 - 9:45	Instruction and Prayer
9:45 - 10:00	Assignments Given/Teams Chosen
10:00 - 12:00	Calling
12:00 - 1:00	Light Lunch and Report Session

It is probably best not to schedule a continuous program of calling without some letup. If you choose Saturday morning, for example, you might schedule eight weeks calling in the fall and another eights weeks in the spring. If your winters are inclement, you can schedule around the cold and rainy months if necessary (although some of the best calling I've ever done has been during a blizzard or rainstorm). A summer calling program can be adapted to the lifestyle of the congregation.

Step Four

Through the triple alliance of prayer, study, and action, your congregation should be well on the road to the development of a genuine ministry of believers. *A calling program in the community is only one expression of congregational participation in ministry.*

Step Five

In a smaller community, a thriving congregation may need to wait for a new harvest to develop.

Then may be the time to move toward the goal of helping each member of the congregation develop his/her potential as a minister for Christ.

A study of *THE EQUIPPING MINISTRY* should assist the congregation in this endeavor. Help each member of the class find a meaningful ministry during the period of study. Once again all your efforts will be multiplied if you use the *STUDY GUIDE.*

Step Six

Remember, new Christians often become the most zealous workers in the harvest fields of the Lord. Help them develop their gifts from the Holy Spirit for the work of Christ. Let them join the multiplied thousands who are praying and working daily for strengthened and growing congregations.

Ordering Information

The entire American Church Growth Study Series is available from STANDARD PUBLISHING, 8121 Hamilton Avenue, Cincinnati, OH 45231. Tel: 513/931-4050.

The same series with cassettes is available from WORLD-WIDE PUBLICATIONS, Box 1240, Minneapolis, MN 55440. Tel: 612/336-0940.

Beacon Hill Press (6401 The Paseo, Kansas City, MO 64131) has also printed an edition of *THE GROWING CONGREGATION* to be used for a training program. Write for information about the series if you are interested.

JOB-DESCRIPTION OF MY MINISTRY

_____

_____

_____

_____

_____

_____

_____

_____

_____

_____

_____

_____

_____

_____

_____

_____

_____

_____

_____

_____

_____

_____